Georgina and the Dragon

Margaret Ryan
Illustrated by Ella Okstad

CW00968959

Chapter 1

George and Georgina were twins. They looked exactly the same. Even their mum and dad couldn't always spot the difference. (Can you?)

One day, Georgina said, "When I grow up, I want to ride out into the countryside and have lots of adventures."

"What nonsense!" said her mum. "When you grow up, you'll be a pretty young lady. You will stay at home and sew beautiful pictures."

"That sounds very boring," muttered Georgina.

"No, it doesn't," said George. "When I grow up, I'd like to sew beautiful pictures."

"What nonsense!" said his dad. "When you grow up, you'll be a strong young man. You will go out and fight dragons."

"That sounds very dangerous," muttered George.

"No, it doesn't," said Georgina. "When I grow up, I'd like to fight dragons."

But their mum and dad didn't listen.

They gave George a wooden sword to play with.

They gave Georgina a sewing kit.

George tried out the wooden sword.

First he poked the cat with it.

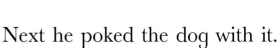
Next he poked the dog with it.

Then he poked his sister with it.

"Ow!" yelled Georgina.

She grabbed the sword and poked George with it.
"Waaaaaaaaaah!" yelled George. "I knew that
fighting would be dangerous. You're much better at it
than I am, Georgina."

Georgina tried out her sewing kit.

First she poked the
needle in her finger.

Next she poked the
needle in her knee.

Then she poked the
needle into George.
"Ow!" yelled George.

He grabbed the needle and sewed up Georgina's sleeves.

"I don't want to sew beautiful pictures," said Georgina. "You're much better at it than I am, George."

"I have an idea," said George. "Why don't we swap places? I'll sew beautiful pictures and you can fight fierce dragons."

"Good idea," said Georgina. "But we must keep it a secret."

Chapter 2

For a while, George and Georgina's secret was safe.
George sewed beautiful pictures.

"Beautiful pictures, Georgina," said Mum.

"Thank you," giggled George.

Georgina was very good with her sword.

"Good work, George," said Dad.

"Thank you," giggled Georgina.

13

Then, one day, word came that a fierce dragon was roaming the countryside.

"It's time for you to go out and fight a real dragon, George," said Dad.

"At last!" cried Georgina.

"Be careful," whispered George.

Georgina took her sword and rode out into the countryside to meet the dragon. Soon she spotted him hiding under a tree. He looked up at Georgina.

"That's a very sharp sword," he said sadly. "I hope you're not going to poke me with it."

"I certainly am," said Georgina.

"Wait a minute!" cried the dragon. "Are you sure you want to hurt me? I'm really a very nice fellow when you get to know me."

A big tear slid down the dragon's cheek and splashed onto his nose.

Georgina was so surprised she dropped her sword. The dragon picked it up and gave it back to her.

"Nasty, dangerous things, swords," he said. "You know, you really shouldn't believe all you hear about dragons. I don't eat people or burn things. In fact, I'm a vegetarian."

"Oh," said Georgina, and she sat down under the tree to think.

The dragon sat down beside her.

"Actually," he said, "I'm glad to have someone to talk to. It's very lonely being a dragon. Everyone runs away when I come near."

"Hmmm," said Georgina, still thinking.

"Everyone except you," said the dragon. "You don't seem to be afraid at all."

"I'm afraid to go home and say I didn't kill you," said Georgina.

And she told the dragon all about swapping places with George.

"If anyone finds out I'm really a girl, George will have to go out and fight dragons. He'd hate that."

"Hmmm," said the dragon, and he had a think too.

Then he had an idea.

"Tell you what," he said. "You pretend to be George, and I'll pretend to be a fierce dragon. You can chase me all over the countryside. We'll have some great adventures."

"Good idea," said Georgina. "But I'll have to tell George."

"Can he keep a secret?" asked the dragon.

"Oh yes," said Georgina.

So Georgina went back home and told George what had happened.

"I'd like to meet the dragon some day," said George, and he picked up his needle.

Georgina picked up her sword and rode out to meet the dragon.

And George sewed the story of Georgina and the Dragon into a beautiful picture.

It still hangs on the wall of their castle.

And that's how we know what **really** happened.